SEASHORE, PONDS AND STREAMS

Michael Chinery

RAINBOW ·BOOKS·

A Walk by the Sea

Our seaside walk starts on a cliff-top high above a sandy bay. As you walk over the headland, keep to the narrow path for your own safety, but stop every now and then to look at the view and to examine the rocks. There is an amazing variety of rocks around the British coastline, including sandstone, limestones and the granites pictured here. Limestones include the chalk rocks which produce many of our famous white cliffs. Some of the rocks are more than 1000 million years old, while others have barely seen one million years pass by.

Many of the rocks contain fossils, which are the remains of long-dead plants and animals. Limestones are particularly rich in fossils, including the remains of sea shells, while chalk is made almost entirely of the shells of microscopic sea creatures called forams. The existence of all these marine fossils proves that the rocks were formed under the sea, and that the Earth has undergone immense changes.

You can see some of these changes in progress at the foot of the headland. Here the sea is at war with the land and you can see the waves battering the rocks and breaking pieces away. It will be millions of years before the cliffs disappear, but they will crumble into the sea eventually. Their fragments will be compressed into new rocks on the sea bed and, far into the future, they will be pushed up again to form fresh land.

Look down along the coast from your cliff-top position. If the tide is out you may be able to see that the higher parts of the shore are shingle while the lower parts are sandy. This is because the incoming waves can throw pebbles far up the beach but the backwash is not strong enough to carry them down again. You may also see rows of wooden or concrete groynes sticking out into the sea. These protect the beaches of resorts. Notice how the sand or shingle builds up on one side of each groyne. Waves always come in at an angle, and sweep the sand and shingle along the beach rather than straight up. Without

The Seashore Code

1. Respect the plants and animals living on the shore.
2. Never throw rubbish of any kind into the water: it can cause pollution and harm wildlife.
3. Test the bottom carefully when investigating plantlife or paddling. Keep away from thick mud.
4. Always find out the times of high tide. Don't get trapped by incoming waves.

A Walk by the Sea

the groynes, the sand and shingle would be swept away from one end of the beach and piled up at the other end. This process is called longshore drift.

As you continue your walk across the cliffs take a good look at the many beautiful flowers that manage to survive the windy conditions and the salty spray. The pictures on the right will help you identify some of them. Thrift, also known as sea pink, turns the cliff-tops and ledges pink in summer. You will probably see and hear many sea birds squabbling over seats on the narrow ledges. You might find them nesting on the ledges in the spring, but don't be tempted to get too near the edge to look at them.

After a while, the cliffs begin to get lower and the path drops down to a small sandy bay. You have left the hard rocks of the headland and moved on to an outcrop of softer rock. The waves have been able to eat into this and have carved out the bay. Here the beach is protected by headlands on each side. The bay is lapped by gentle waves which wash in sand but cannot bring in the heavier shingle, so a fine sandy beach has been formed. Behind it, there are a number of dunes – ridges of sand piled up by the wind. Those nearest to the sea are still quite loose, but those further back have been fixed by clumps of tough marram grass and other plants, such as sea holly. The roots of these plants bind the sand together and stop it from being blown about too much. Still further back, the dunes may be covered with turf, heather or other small shrubs.

A small stream runs down to the beach at low tide, but when the tide comes in again the water surges up the stream-bed and over the banks. Fine mud gradually builds up in this area and forms a saltmarsh. Many interesting plants and animals live here and the marsh is an important feeding ground for geese and wading birds, especially in winter.

Tides sweep in twice every day. They are caused by the gravitational pull of the sun and the moon, and this pull varies as the Earth rotates on its axis and the moon rotates around the Earth. High-tide level is therefore not the same every day. Every two weeks at

COMMON COASTAL FLOWERS

Sea Holly

Sea Pea

Thrift

Sea Purslane

Salty Problems

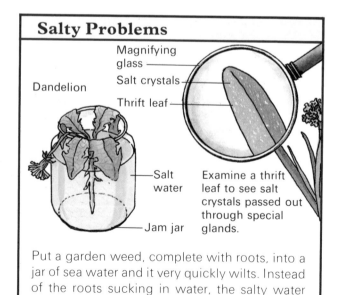

Dandelion

Magnifying glass

Salt crystals

Thrift leaf

Salt water

Jam jar

Examine a thrift leaf to see salt crystals passed out through special glands.

Put a garden weed, complete with roots, into a jar of sea water and it very quickly wilts. Instead of the roots sucking in water, the salty water draws the sap out of the plant. Seaside plants have a very strong sap and can take in water from their salty surroundings.

Glasswort

Sea Lavender

Sea Kale

Seablite

Hottentot Fig

Yellow Horned-poppy

Sea Campion

Right: The estuarine reach of a river, where it joins the sea, is often very muddy. You can see this very easily at low tide. The banks are flooded by the highest tides and the soil is rather salty. These areas are known as salt-marshes and they are often dissected by muddy channels which carry the water away as the tide falls. Only specialized, salt-tolerant plants can grow here, including the thrift which makes the marsh on the right so colourful.

A Rocky Seashore

the time of new and full moons, there are especially strong tides called spring tides. In the days following a spring tide the high-water mark gets progressively lower, and then rises again towards the next spring tide.

Rocky Shores

As we have seen on our short walk, there are several different kinds of seashore and each type supports its own kinds of wildlife. Let's start with a rocky shore.

As the tide goes out you will see that the rocks are clothed with seaweeds in most places. There are many different kinds of seaweeds. Most of them are brown, but there are also green ones and red ones. Select a patch of seaweed growing on the upper half of the shore and note the time at which it is covered by the incoming tide. How many hours pass before it is uncovered again? The higher up the shore your seaweeds are growing, the shorter the period of immersion and the longer the exposure to the air. Different seaweeds can survive different

amounts of exposure, and therefore are found growing in distinct zones on the shore.

The green seaweeds can survive plenty of exposure to air and rain and can grow near the top of the beach. Look for them also where streams of fresh water trickle over the shore. Sea lettuce is a very common species, but the most abundant of the green seaweeds is *Enteromorpha*. This is sometimes called sea grass because it waves about like grass when covered by the tide, but when uncovered it collapses and forms a very slippery mat.

You will also find the brown channelled wrack at the top of the shore, the upper zone. Look carefully at its branching fronds to see the narrow channels which give the plant its name. These hold water and help the plant to survive in the air. There may be some days when these upper-shore seaweeds are not reached by the tide at all, although they are probably splashed by spray every day.

The middle part of the beach is clothed mainly with brown seaweeds, such as toothed wrack and bladder wrack, but even here the

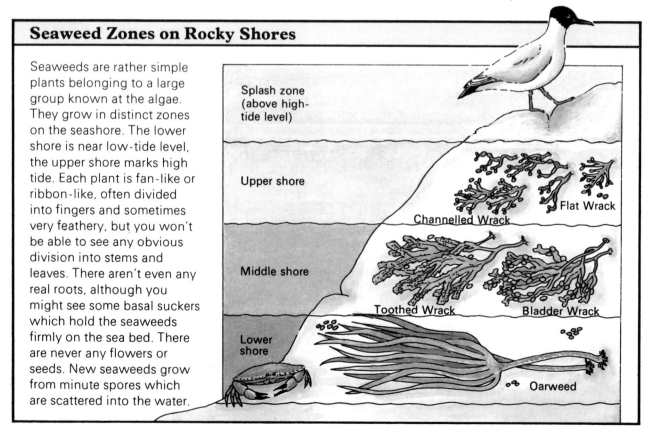

Seaweed Zones on Rocky Shores

Seaweeds are rather simple plants belonging to a large group known at the algae. They grow in distinct zones on the seashore. The lower shore is near low-tide level, the upper shore marks high tide. Each plant is fan-like or ribbon-like, often divided into fingers and sometimes very feathery, but you won't be able to see any obvious division into stems and leaves. There aren't even any real roots, although you might see some basal suckers which hold the seaweeds firmly on the sea bed. There are never any flowers or seeds. New seaweeds grow from minute spores which are scattered into the water.

Splash zone (above high-tide level)

Upper shore

Middle shore

Lower shore

Channelled Wrack

Flat Wrack

Toothed Wrack

Bladder Wrack

Oarweed

species are clearly zoned. The toothed wrack, which you can recognize by its saw-like edges, will not grow if exposed to the air for more than about six hours at a time, and so it is confined to a zone below mid-tide level. Bladder wrack, recognized by the air-filled bladders on its fronds, can withstand more exposure than the toothed wrack, but not as much as the channelled wrack. It therefore occupies a zone between the two.

The largest seaweeds around our coasts are the brown oarweeds, such as the sea belt, that grow in dense 'forests' just below low-water mark. You can sometimes see these seaweeds just poking out of the water at the lowest tides, but you will more often find them thrown up on the beach after a storm. The sea belt may be as much as nine metres long.

Red seaweeds are generally rather small and delicate and they cannot survive out of water for very long. Look for them on the lowest parts of the shore and also in rock pools. Many of them are coated with chalky material and become white when they die.

The Strand Line

Each tide brings in an assortment of seaweed, shells and other debris. Much of this is left in the strand line at high-water mark. You will find an amazing variety of small animals amongst the debris. Seagulls and other birds know this as well: watch them scurrying along the strand line and turning over the seaweed as they search for food.

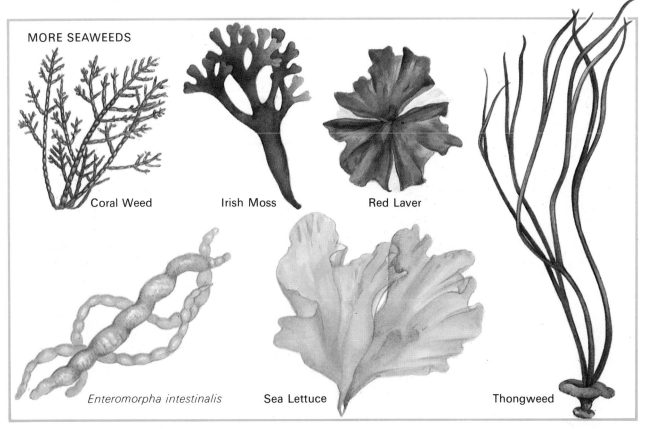

MORE SEAWEEDS

Coral Weed

Irish Moss

Red Laver

Enteromorpha intestinalis

Sea Lettuce

Thongweed

Animals on the Rocks

Animals on the Rocks

The seaweeds provide food and shelter for many animals. Try searching through a patch of weeds at low tide. It won't take long to find the periwinkles – small sea snails that browse on the seaweeds. Look out also for the attractive top shells, shaped just like old-fashioned spinning tops. Put some of the shells into a bucket or dish of sea water so you can see the animals crawling about.

You will find the conical shells of the common limpet all over the rocks. A sudden knock with a stone may dislodge the animal, but otherwise it is almost impossible to remove it. Even the full force of the waves crashing on to the rocks cannot overcome the limpet's astonishing grip, but when completely submerged the limpet relaxes its grip and wanders off to feed. Although its shell is not coiled, the limpet is just another sea snail and, like all snails, it has a tongue like a strip of sandpaper. It uses this tongue to scrape small seaweeds from the rocks. In places where there are lots of limpets the rocks are almost bare. After feeding, the limpet always returns to the same resting place, and gradually wears a circular groove in the rock. Each limpet fits its home extremely well.

Browsing Periwinkles

Under the blanket of damp weed, periwinkles can carry on feeding even when the tide is out. The two kinds of periwinkles you are most likely to find are the flat periwinkle whose shell is normally yellow or brown and the common periwinkle with its black or brownish shell. This is the winkle sold in fish shops and stalls.

In some places the waves are a little too strong for seaweeds to survive on the rocks, and this is where the barnacles take over. Their conical white shells are sometimes so numerous that you cannot put a pencil point between them. The barnacles can live in such dense colonies because the tides are always bringing in fresh food supplies. Young barnacles float in the water for a while before settling down on the rocks. If they are to survive they must land in an area where they are submerged long enough for them to get sufficient food, but they must also be exposed

Painting Limpets

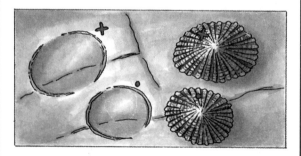

Look for limpets at low tide and mark a few with blobs of quick-drying paint. Put similar marks on the rock nearby. You will find the limpets in exactly the same spot the next day, but if you could watch them when the tide is in you would see that they move away to feed on algae (as above). Notice the scars on the rock, formed by friction between the shells and the rock.

Observing Barnacles

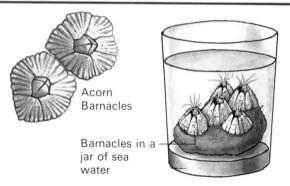

Acorn Barnacles

Barnacles in a jar of sea water

Look for some barnacles on a small stone that you can put into a dish of sea water. You can then see these strange little animals at work. Under the water they open their shells and push out feathery limbs which rhythmically comb the water for food particles. Return them to the place you found them after the experiment.

to the air for a few hours each day. Many young barnacles fail to find suitable places, but their fate is not left entirely to chance. The youngsters are attracted by the scent of existing colonies and they tend to settle near them – in places which are obviously suitable for barnacle growth.

The dark blue shells of mussels often cluster on the same rocks as the barnacles, attached by bunches of strong threads. Like the barnacles, they depend on the tides and waves to bring their food. The shells open slightly when they are under water and, just like the cockles, the mussels suck in streams of water and filter microscopic plants and other food from it.

If you examine mussel and barnacle colonies you might well see some of the sea snails called dog whelks. Their shells are generally yellow or white, often with brown or black bands, and they are extremely thick – a necessity if they are to survive the pounding of the rough water around the rocks. Unlike the periwinkles and top shells, the dog whelks are flesh-eaters. Look at empty mussel shells thrown up on the beach: many will have a small hole near the apex (tip), showing where a dog whelk got to work. Barnacles are also

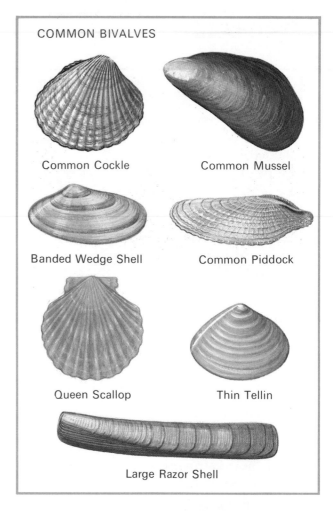

COMMON BIVALVES

Common Cockle

Common Mussel

Banded Wedge Shell

Common Piddock

Queen Scallop

Thin Tellin

Large Razor Shell

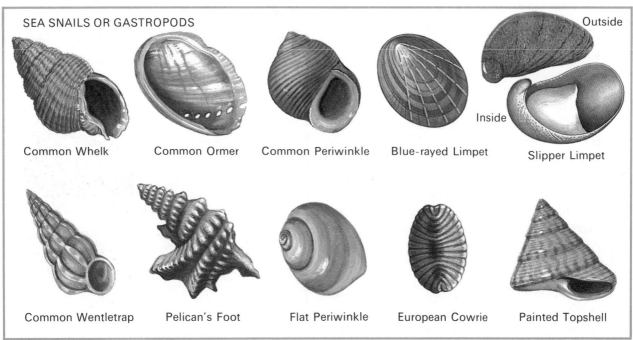

SEA SNAILS OR GASTROPODS

Common Whelk

Common Ormer

Common Periwinkle

Blue-rayed Limpet

Outside

Inside

Slipper Limpet

Common Wentletrap

Pelican's Foot

Flat Periwinkle

European Cowrie

Painted Topshell

Rock Crevices

Tempting a Crab

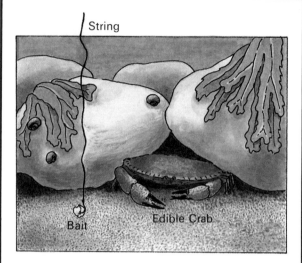

String

Bait   Edible Crab

Try tempting out a crab with a piece of meat or fish — perhaps a dead crab or starfish from the strand line. Tie the food to a piece of string and dangle it by a crevice in the rocks. If your crab comes out to investigate, let it grab the food with its great claws: it may hold on so tightly that you can lift it out.

eaten by these carnivorous snails, but they are less nutritious than mussels and the dog whelks feeding in a barnacle colony tend to be smaller than those feeding on mussels. They usually have paler shells as well.

Rock Crevices

Rock crevices are good places to explore. Many animals hide here to escape the drying action of the sun and wind. High on the shore you will find the woodlouse-like sea slater, which comes out at night to feed on decaying seaweed and other rubbish. Lower down you may find various kinds of crabs. They venture out on dull days, but scuttle rapidly back into their crevices if they see you. Crabs are greedy scavengers and find it hard to resist the smell of food. Try tempting one out into the open and watch its curious sideways walk. Notice its stalked eyes and quivering antennae.

While exploring the crevices you will probably see some blobs of red jelly. They don't look much like animals, but they are sea

anemones safely tucked up until the tide returns. They are beautiful animals, but to see their flower-like beauty you need to investigate the rocks just below low-tide level. Here, if the water is clear, you will see the animals unfolded and waving their slender arms or tentacles. But don't be misled by their flower-like appearance: the anemones are death-traps for fishes and other small animals. The tentacles are clothed with hundreds of minute stings which are fired

Starfish Movement

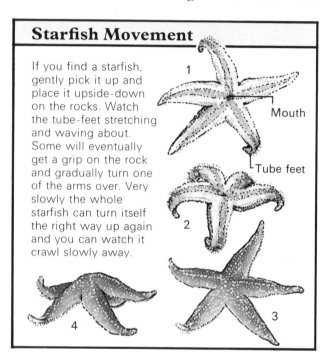

If you find a starfish, gently pick it up and place it upside-down on the rocks. Watch the tube-feet stretching and waving about. Some will eventually get a grip on the rock and gradually turn one of the arms over. Very slowly the whole starfish can turn itself the right way up again and you can watch it crawl slowly away.

Mouth

Tube feet

1

2

3

4

Dog Whelks

Dog whelks use their rough tongues to drill through the shells of mussels, and then rasp out the soft flesh. The tongue then carries the rasped-out food into the dog whelk's mouth. No drilling is needed for the barnacles: the dog whelk merely forces back the small chalky plates at the top of the shell to get at the animal inside.

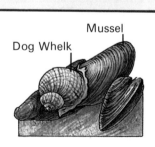

Mussel

Dog Whelk

Common Dog Whelk

into any animal that brushes against the anemone. Small animals are quickly paralysed and then pulled into the anemone's mouth. You can watch the process by tying a small piece of meat or fish to a length of cotton and dangling it in the anemone's tentacles. These will immediately coil around the food and drag or push it into the mouth. It all happens very quickly.

The clear water around low-tide level is a superb place for observing those animals that can't stay out of the water for long. Here you can watch shrimps and prawns darting about in company with various small fishes, and you can also find many prickly sea urchins. Be careful not to tread on these animals when paddling, because their spines can make your feet very sore. On some of the softer rocks the urchins carve out little hollows for themselves and stay there permanently.

Starfishes of various kinds find plenty of other animals to eat in the shallows. Pick up a starfish and look at the underside: the arms are covered with little suckers called tube-feet. The starfish uses these to cling to the rocks and to clamber over the surface. These powerful suckers are also used when feeding on cockles and other bivalves. They are so strong that they can pull the two halves of the shell apart: the starfish can then feed on the soft body inside.

Fascinating Rock Pools

Waves and the stones that they carry wear away some parts of the rocks more quickly than others. When the tide goes out each of these hollows remains full of water and is transformed into a natural aquarium. Here you can watch all kinds of seashore animals going about their lives just as if the tide were in. It is usually easier to watch animals in a pool than at low-water mark: there are no waves lapping around them, and you also have more time because the pools may be exposed for several hours. At low-water mark you have only a few minutes before the tide turns and comes in again.

Rock pools often have pink linings, produced by small red seaweeds whose flat fronds are encrusted with lime. Numerous

Above: Hermit crabs have long soft bodies, which they protect by taking up residence in empty shells. As they grow, the crabs move house to larger shells.
Right: A rock pool with clumps of mussels and attendant dog whelks, a sea anemone in the middle, and a sea urchin which has camouflaged itself with small stones.

Rock Pools

sea snails browse on these and other seaweeds. Look out for shells moving across the bottom rather faster than normal. These will contain hermit crabs which protect their soft bodies by occupying empty snail shells. Look carefully, too, for small prawns on the bottom of the pools. They are not easy to see because they are almost transparent, but a pattern of red dots and streaks may give away their position. The chameleon prawn, which has a strongly arched back and is much smaller than the common prawn, can actually change colour to match sandy or weedy backgrounds in the pools.

Sea anemones flourish in rock pools because they are always underwater and can feed all day instead of spending half their time folded inwards to prevent themselves drying out. Look out for the snakelocks anemone. Its body is greenish brown, but the tentacles are lighter green and usually marked with red and white. The tentacles cannot be pulled right into the body and this anemone cannot survive on rocks which are exposed to the air.

Looking into a rock pool is not always easy, especially on a sunny day when there are many surface reflections. One way to solve

Observing Rock Pools

You can make a simple but effective viewer from a small plastic bucket or large yoghurt pot, a sheet of stretch plastic and a rubber band. Cut the bottom from the bucket or yoghurt pot and stretch the plastic over it. Fix firmly with the rubber band. Push the bottom of the bucket into the water and look through it.

Cut out the bottom and stretch plastic film over it.

Rubber band

Old bucket

this problem is to wear a diving mask. Or make a viewing screen as described above. If neither of these methods is possible, you can rig up some sort of sunshade to keep the sun's rays away from the pool. A small aquarium net will be useful for catching prawns and other small creatures. Tip them into a dish of sea water so that you can see them properly. Don't leave the dish in the sun, and remember to return the animals to the pool after you have looked at them.

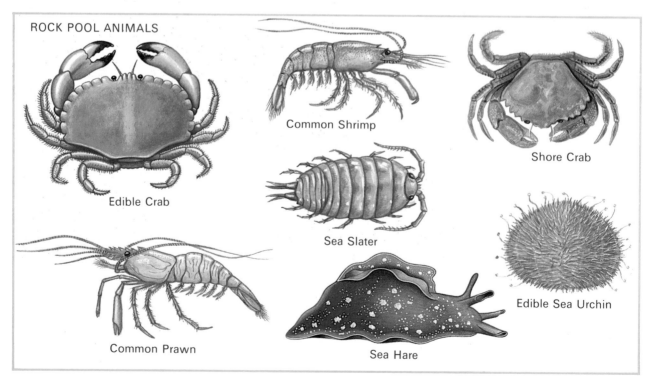

ROCK POOL ANIMALS

Edible Crab

Common Shrimp

Shore Crab

Sea Slater

Edible Sea Urchin

Common Prawn

Sea Hare

The Sandy Shore

Life on the Sandy Shore

When the tide goes out over a sandy shore it leaves a blank sheet of sand. There aren't even any seaweeds, for they can't anchor themselves to the shifting sand. But the shore isn't really lifeless: if the top 30 centimetres of sand could be spirited away you would find a thick carpet of wriggling bodies. These animals burrow into the sand when the tide recedes and wait for it to return. The sand stays moist and the animals are in no danger of drying up.

Near the top of the beach you would find innumerable sand hoppers – small shrimp-like animals that live around high-water mark and come out to feed on the strand-line debris at night. Lower down on the shore you would find a few sea snails, together with shrimps and starfishes and a few sea urchins, but the great majority of the sand-dwellers are worms and bivalve molluscs. These molluscs, such as the cockles and razor shells and the beautiful pink tellins, have shells consisting of two valves hinged along one edge. They burrow through the sand with the aid of a muscular foot, and they move up to feed at the surface of the sand when the tide is in.

You might wonder what all these thousands of animals find to eat on the bare sand, but the tide actually washes in more than enough food for them. When the tide is in, the sea bed receives a constant rain of debris in the form of fragments of plants and dead animals and animal droppings, and it is this debris that feeds the bulk of the sea-bed creatures. Collect a jar of water from the incoming waves and you will see just how much sediment it carries.

The lugworm merely swallows the sand and mud and digests any food in it, but other animals have rather more refined methods of collecting their food. They are known as filter feeders. Many of the worms wriggle to the surface of the sand when the tide comes in and then expand a crown of feathery tentacles which trap the falling sediment and waft it into the mouth. Often known as fan worms, from the shape of their crowns, many are beautifully and delicately coloured. Most of them live in tubes which they build from sand

particles cemented together with slime from their bodies. You can sometimes see these tubes poking out of the sand at low tide, but the worms are then hunched up right down at the bottom.

You can watch the filter-feeding action of the bivalves quite easily if you can find a live cockle or tellin in the sand or mud of the lower shore. Put your cockle into a jam jar

Above: Look for the turnstone on rocky and weedy beaches in winter. It is well-named, for it uses its beak to flip over stones in search of food.

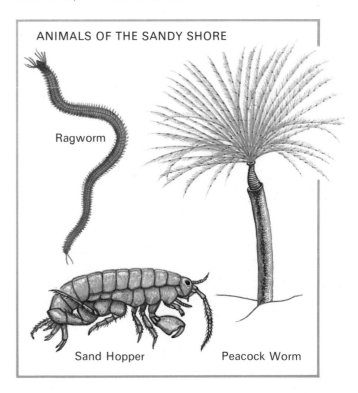

ANIMALS OF THE SANDY SHORE

Ragworm

Sand Hopper

Peacock Worm

Barren Shingle

Feeding a Cockle and a Tellin

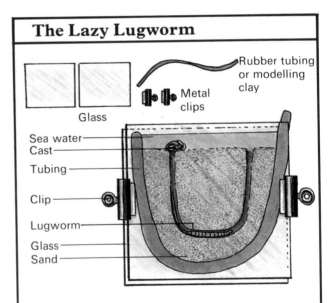

Put a cockle into a jam jar with enough sand for it to bury itself and then fill the jar with sea water. As the water clears you will see the cockle's two frilly breathing tubes or siphons just above the sand. Use a simple eye-dropper to squirt a few drops of gravy or soup just above the cockle and watch the food stream into one of the siphons. Put a tellin into another jar and watch its siphons hoovering up the sand. Notice that one of its siphons is much larger than the other.

containing sand and sea water – see above. Let the water clear and you will see two frilly tubes just poking through the sand. These are the cockle's breathing tubes or siphons. Water is sucked in through one tube, passed over the gills, and pumped out through the other tube. The gills take oxygen from the water and also filter out any food particles and pass them to the mouth. The tellin feeds rather differently. One of its siphons is very long and is used rather like the hose of a vacuum cleaner to suck debris from the sea bed, but the water and debris is still filtered through the gills.

The bivalves themselves are eaten by starfishes and some flesh-eating snails. Like the rock-living dog whelks, these snails bore holes in the bivalve shells to get at the flesh inside. Keep an eye open for drilled shells on the beach. Oystercatchers and other wading birds also eat lots of bivalves. Watch the birds probing for them in the sand and mud: with binoculars, you might be able to see how they open the shells with their beaks.

Barren Shingle

Shingle beaches generally develop on exposed coasts, where the strong waves can hurl the stones high on the beach. You often find a ridge of very large stones right at the top of the beach, thrown there by storm waves during the highest tides. Very few animals can live in the shingle because they would be crushed as the stones tumble about, but you might find a few sea slaters around high-water mark. Water shortage is also a problem, because water drains away very quickly through the shingle. Seaweeds can't establish themselves on the rolling stones, but a few flowering plants manage to grow in the shingle just above high-water mark. Long roots reach down to the moisture and also anchor the plants securely in the moving

The Lazy Lugworm

To make this mini-aquarium fit a strip of modelling clay or a length of rubber tubing between two pieces of glass (each about 25 cm square) so that they are about 1 cm apart. Use the clips to hold the glass firmly so that sand and sea water can be held in the U-shaped chamber. Put a lugworm on the surface and watch it make its L-shaped burrow. It will soon start to feed by sucking sand in through the mouth. This causes the tell-tale depression in the sand above it. Food particles in the sand are digested and the sand itself is later pushed out from the hind end to make worm casts on the surface.

SEASHORE FISHES

Sand Smelt

Shanny

Butterfish

Sea Horse

Lesser Weever

Nilsson's Pipefish

Common Goby

Below: Most fishes go out with the tide. If you want to get a proper look at them you can use a shrimping net. Push it gently along the sand in the shallows; it will catch several of the fishes shown above, as well as numerous shrimps.

shingle. The sea sandwort forms bright green mats over the shingle in many places, while here and there you will find the beautiful sea pea and the yellow horned-poppy.

Birds of the Beaches

The most noticeable birds around the seashore are the gulls. You can see them even in busy resorts, gliding over the beaches and swooping down in noisy gangs in search of food. They are real scavengers and their strong beaks can deal with most kinds of food: they can even crack open the shells of crabs to get at the juicy meat inside. The birds pay great attention to the water's edge, where crabs and other small animals may be stranded, and they are quite likely to steal your sandwiches if you are not careful.

Keep your eyes open for the different kinds of gulls. Three are very common, but you might well see five or six different kinds. The herring gull is so common that it has become a pest in some places: it covers buildings with its droppings and also eats the eggs and nestlings of other birds on nature reserves. Its back is light to dark grey and its legs are usually pink. The lesser black-backed gull is similar, but a little smaller, and generally has a darker back. Its legs are usually yellow. The black-headed gull is another abundant

Seaside Birds

species. You can recognize it very easily in summer by its black head and wing-tips and its dark red beak. In the winter the head becomes white, with just a brownish patch behind the eye. All three kinds of gulls nest on the ground on dunes and saltmarshes, but the herring gull also nests on cliffs. The black-headed gull nests far inland as well as by the sea, and many of these gulls never actually see the sea in their lives. Look for them around rubbish dumps and reservoirs.

The terns are closely related to the gulls but they are much daintier birds, with pointed beaks and long, forked tails. Watch them fluttering just above the waves with their beaks pointing straight down as they look for fish. You might see them hover for a while and then plunge into the water to snatch up a fish. Terns lay their eggs on sand or shingle, without building any real nest.

Above: Rugged cliffs make excellent nesting sites for gulls and other sea birds because few enemies can reach them. Most of the gulls here are kittiwakes, whose nests are made with grass, mud and seaweed.

SEA BIRDS

male
female
Shelduck

Common Tern

dark-bellied form
light-bellied form
Brent Goose

female
male
Long-tailed Duck

Fulmar
winter

summer

British form
Scandinavian form

Guillemot

Lesser Black-backed Gull

Razorbill

To see some of the many other kinds of sea-birds you will have to visit wilder parts of the coastline. Many of these birds come ashore only in the spring breeding season and spend the rest of the year fishing out at sea, often very far away from land. These birds include gannets, guillemots, razorbills, and the comical puffins. They all like to breed on rugged cliffs, especially on small islands and other remote areas, and there may be many thousands of them nesting in a small area. These nesting colonies are best seen from out at sea and sight-seeing boat trips are often available from nearby harbours.

Wading birds flock to the shore at low tide to probe the mud and sand with their long beaks, hoping to find worms and shellfish. Use your binoculars (see page 31) to watch them feeding. Winter is the best time to see the waders because many species spend the summer on the Arctic tundra. Many ducks and geese also fly down from the north to spend the winter on our seashore.

The spring and autumn migration periods are especially exciting for the seashore bird-watcher, for this is when we see the passage migrants such as the curlew sandpiper and the little stint – birds which breed in the far north and then fly to Africa for the winter. They use the shores of western Europe as refuelling stops. But it is not only water birds that can be found on the coast during the migration periods. Many of the summer visitors to our fields and woodlands come from Africa and they find the shore a welcome resting place after their long sea crossings. They may feed around the shore for several days before flying on to look for inland nesting sites. These birds may also gather on the shore before leaving again in the autumn.

Continental form

Atlantic form

summer

winter

Cormorant

Puffin

Redshank

Ringed Plover

Little Ringed Plover

Oystercatcher

summer

winter

Turnstone

Gannet

A Walk by a River

The stream gleams as it flows over its bed of stones and gravel. The water is shallow in most places and banks of gravel break the surface in several spots. But here and there, especially on the outsides of the bends, there are some deeper pools. The water is clear and you can see small shoals of fishes darting about. Most of them are less than five centimetres long. They are minnows, and this stretch of river is the minnow reach – one of five major zones found in a typical river. As we look far upstream, we can see the distant hills where the river begins its journey to the sea as a little trickle between moss-covered boulders. This trickle is known as the headstream. Soon it is joined by other trickles, and the increased flow of water carries all the small stones and debris away. The stream now has a rocky bed dotted with large boulders. This stretch is called the troutbeck, for the trout is one of the few fishes that can swim in the fast-moving water. Our minnow reach is below the troutbeck.

Graceful alder trees grow here and there on the banks of the minnow reach. They are easily identified by the small cone-like female catkins. Some are green and still contain developing seeds, but others are hard and woody, with scales gaping to show where the seeds have escaped. In some places the cattle come down for a drink and churn up the ground at the water's edge. Look for the water-starwort growing here – on the mud and in the shallows. It gets its name from the star-shaped clusters of leaves which float at the tips of its stems. Out in the stream, anchored in the gravel, the submerged stems and hair-like leaves of the water-crowfoot trail in the swift current. Minnows are abundant in the water, but trout live here as well. A splash, together with tell-tale circular ripples, tells us that a trout has leapt up to catch an insect flying too close to the water surface. Stickle-backs wriggle in and out of the water-crowfoot, while the

The Water Code

1. Avoid damaging banks and waterside vegetation.
2. Never throw rubbish of any kind on to the banks or into the water.
3. Don't disturb the water where people are fishing.
4. Test the bottom carefully when investigating plantlife or paddling. Keep away from thick mud.
5. Never explore the water-side by yourself.

very spiny miller's thumb or bullhead lurks under the stones. The kingfisher enjoys fishing in the minnow reach. You will probably see no more than a bright blue flash as it skims past, but you might be lucky enough to find its regular perch.

As we follow the narrow riverside path downstream, the surrounding land gradually gets flatter and the river begins to slow down. A tributary joins in and the river widens, but it does not flow any faster. The water is muddy, and lots of mud is deposited along the edges. Bulrushes and many other plants, including great willowherb and yellow iris, are found on these muddy banks. This is the river's lowland reach, also known as the bream reach because the bream is one of the commoner fishes in the murky water. Other fishes include carp, roach, rudd, perch and pike. Swans, coots and moorhens all nest and feed here, and the heron finds much of its food in the shallows.

The lowland reach stretches for a long way, sweeping across the countryside in broad curves. In the far distance lies its final zone – the estuarine reach where the river ends its journey and joins the sea.

Rivers at Work

The enormous amounts of water on the Earth are constantly being circulated. The circulation is known as the water cycle and is powered by the sun. Water evaporates from the surface of the ocean and rises into the air as water vapour. This vapour later condenses and falls as rain or snow. Much of it goes straight back into the sea, but a good deal falls on the land.

Water falling on the very hard and less porous rocks simply runs over the surface and is channelled into small streams. These are the headstreams which are the beginnings of the rivers. Water falling on to softer or more porous rocks, such as chalk or sandstone,

Waterfalls

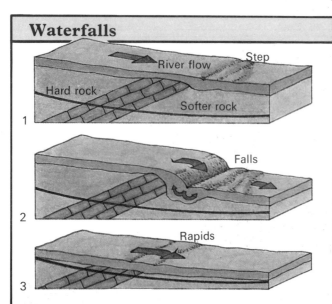

Waterfalls develop when a river runs from a layer of hard rock on to a softer one. The softer rock is worn away more rapidly, leaving the hard one standing up as a step (1). The water rushes over this, and the force of the falling water erodes the softer rock even more quickly. The falls thus get higher and higher (2). But they are not permanent features. The river gradually eliminates them in its struggle to achieve its smooth curve or profile. Slowly it

wears away the lip of the falls until eventually they degenerate into rapids, and then disappear altogether (3). The spray thrown up from the waterfall ensures that the surrounding rocks are always wet, and they support a wealth of ferns, mosses, liverworts and other moisture-loving plants (see above). But remember that waterfalls are dangerous places. The rocks are slippery because of the damp vegetation.

From Pond to Dry Land

Ponds and lakes are simply temporary interruptions of the water cycle, holding up water for a while and delaying its return to the sea. Over hundreds, or even millions of years, these areas of fresh water are converted to dry land through the natural processes of succession. It is possible to see marked changes in a pond or a small lake in just a few years. Mud and silt accumulate on the bottom and the pond gradually gets shallower. The reeds and other emergent plants reach out towards the middle as the mud builds up. Dead leaves and other debris collect around the bases of the plants and, before long, the debris rises above the water level in the shallow area around the margin. The swamp plants die out and the marsh plants spread in from the banks. All the open water eventually disappears, being replaced first by swamp and then by marsh. Finally the pond may be converted to dry land.

Above: Lowland ponds like the one pictured here are usually full of nutrients and have plenty of plants growing in them. They are also rich in animal life, with lots of fishes and insects.

soaks into them instead of running over the surface. It generally seeps into the rivers lower down, but it may form its own river by bubbling out of the ground as a spring.

Whatever their origins, the rivers all pour the water back to the sea. But rivers are not just water-carriers. They provide homes for large numbers of plants and animals, and they also play a major role in shaping the land. The water itself can cut a channel by dissolving the rocks – but only very slowly. Much more effective, especially in upland regions, is the action of the vast numbers of stones swept along on the river bed. The stones act like giant ribbons of sandpaper to wear away the river bed and cut the valley deeper and deeper into the hills. In the process, the stones themselves are worn down, and by the time they get to the lower reaches of the river they have been ground down to fine silt and mud.

If the river meets a hollow on its way down to the sea it will turn it into a lake but only until the river can find a way out. The natural processes of succession (see box above) will gradually convert the lake into dry land with the river flowing through it. The river's aim is to produce a smooth curve or profile from its source to the sea, but millions of years are needed before it achieves this.

Still Waters

Still waters are traditionally divided into lakes and ponds. The larger bodies of water are the lakes, while the smaller ones are generally known as ponds. But there is no fixed size at which a pond becomes a lake. Lakes, however, are generally of natural origin and often very deep. Many have streams running in and out of them, although the bulk of the water remains quite still. Ponds are relatively shallow. Some may be entirely natural, formed when rainwater accumulates in hollows on clay or other non-porous rocks, but most ponds have been made by people. Farm and village ponds, for example, were usually dug out to provide watering places for cattle and horses. No longer needed for this purpose, many ponds are unfortunately disappearing. And with them we are losing the wildlife that lives in and around the water. Naturalists everywhere are trying to save the ponds that are left.

Pond Plant Zones

The surrounding rocks play an important part in determining the types and amounts of wildlife in and around the water. Hard rocks, found mainly in upland regions, release small amounts of minerals to the water. As a result vegetation tends to be sparse around the upland lakes, with just occasional patches of reeds sprouting from the stony shores and a few scattered patches of pondweed on the surface. Even the microscopic floating plants that form the plankton are relatively scarce, and the water is generally very clear. Such lakes are often called *oligotrophic*, which means nutritionally poor. But don't think that they have no animal life at all. Quite a number of caddis flies and stoneflies grow up in these lakes, along with numerous small midges. Their youngsters find enough food in the form of algae and assorted debris on the lake bed, and in turn are eaten by trout and charr – the two main fishes.

Lowland waters tell a very different story. The clays and other relatively soft rocks yield abundant minerals and the waters of both lakes and ponds are very rich. These mineral-rich waters are often called *eutrophic*, which means highly nutritious, and they teem with plant and animal life.

Pond Plant Zones

The plants growing in and around a pond form distinct zones according to the depth of the water. You can investigate this for yourself if you have a suitable pond in your area. Wear wellingtons to wade into the pond but test the firmness of the bottom before each step and don't go on if the bottom is very muddy.

Some pond plants do not actually like to stand in water for very long, and you will find these only on the surrounding banks. They are called marsh plants. Their roots enjoy the damp soil, but the stems remain fairly dry. Common marsh plants which you might find around your pond include marsh marigold, purple loosestrife, great willowherb, common comfrey and water forget-me-not. Right at the water's edge, with water lapping regularly around their bases, grow the swamp plants. These include the yellow iris, bur-

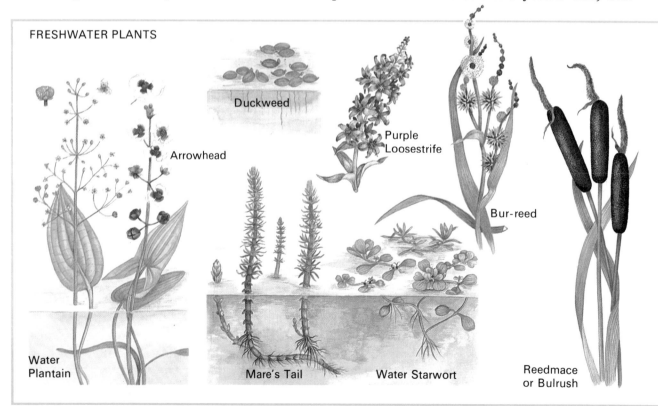

FRESHWATER PLANTS

Duckweed

Arrowhead

Purple Loosestrife

Bur-reed

Water Plantain

Mare's Tail

Water Starwort

Reedmace or Bulrush

reeds, bulrushes, mare's tail and various large grasses that we call reeds. There are also several sedges, which you can recognize by their triangular stems. Many of these plants extend out to depths of about 15 centimetres and they are commonly called *emergent* plants – because the roots are under the water but the stems and leaves emerge into the air. The arrowhead is a particularly interesting member of this group because it has three very different kinds of leaves. The aerial leaves are shaped just like the heads of arrows and they stand well above the water, but the plant also has oval leaves which float on the surface and very thin, strap-shaped leaves which always remain under the water.

Beyond the reeds and other emergent plants you will probably find many completely submerged species, such as curled pondweed and hornwort. There may also be water lilies and broad-leaved pondweed, both rooted on the bottom but with floating leaves. Scattered among them may be some completely free-floating plants such as frogbit and water soldier. Beware of the latter, for its

Light-loving Algae

Fill a jam jar with green pond water and wrap it in black polythene or aluminium foil to keep out the light. Cover the top as well as the sides, and then cut a hole about 1 cm across in the wrapping on one side. Stand the jar on a window sill with the hole facing the light. Carefully remove the wrapping after a few hours. Have the green algae gathered in the lighted area?

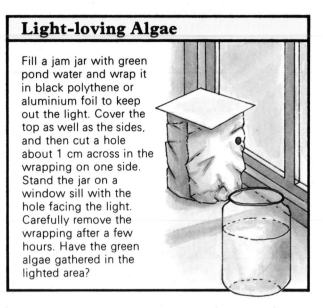

leaves are edged with very sharp teeth which can cut you very easily. Water lilies sometimes grow in water as much as two metres deep, but generally they prefer shallower water. The free-floating plants, on the other hand, can grow anywhere. But you won't find many at the edge because they would be shaded out by the emergent species.

Great Willowherb

Marsh Marigold

Indian Balsam

Investigating Water-weeds

Make a simple drag from three pieces of stout wire bent to form hooks. Attach it to a short stick and tie a long string to the end. Use it for dragging weeds from a pond. Use a stick to measure the depth of water at different distances from the bank and then list the plants occuring at each depth. Watch out for animals crawling among the weeds.

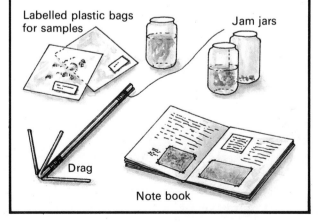

Labelled plastic bags for samples

Jam jars

Drag

Note book

Animals of the Pond

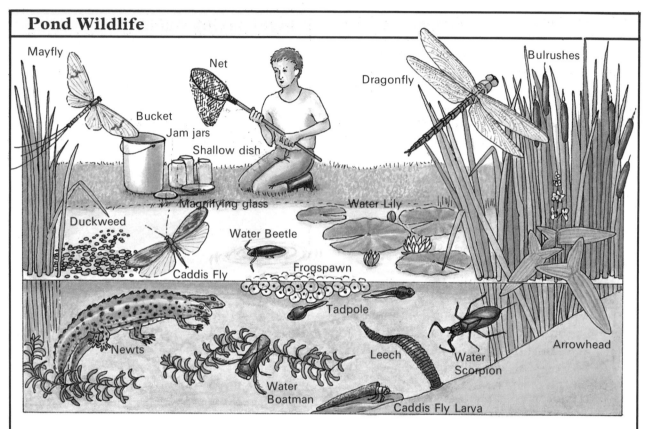

Pond Wildlife

Mayfly
Net
Dragonfly
Bulrushes
Bucket
Jam jars
Shallow dish
Duckweed
Magnifying glass
Water Lily
Water Beetle
Caddis Fly
Frogspawn
Tadpole
Newts
Leech
Water Scorpion
Arrowhead
Water Boatman
Caddis Fly Larva

To explore pond wildlife buy a small aquarium net from a pet shop or make one from a length of strong wire and a piece of muslin or the foot of an old nylon stocking. Bend the wire into a circle roughly 15 centimetres across and sew the net bag to it. You can then fix your net to a handle about one metre long. It is a good idea to flatten one side of the net frame, for this makes it easier to push the net across the bottom of the pond. Take a few shallow dishes and a hand lens or magnifying glass to examine creatures on the spot. Dishes with white bottoms are best, although clear glass will be fine if you stand them on white paper. A bucket and jam jars are useful for holding samples. Don't forget to return all the animals and plants to the pond when you have finished looking at them.

Tiny duckweeds float on nearly all ponds and are sometimes so numerous that they completely cover the surface with a brilliant green carpet. Take a spoonful of these little plants and float them in a jar of water. See how each plant consists of just a flattened disc, known as a *thallus*. Notice the thread-like roots hanging down into the water. During the spring and summer each thallus produces a succession of buds, which eventually break off and form new plants. Within days, these new plants are producing buds themselves, and this is how the duckweed spreads so rapidly over a pond. The plants also produce flowers and seeds at certain times. The flowers have no petals and they are too small to be seen without a powerful magnifying glass. They develop in tiny pouches at the edge of the thallus.

The duckweeds are among the smallest of all flowering plants, but they are by no means the smallest plants in the pond. This honour goes to the microscopic algae that swim in the water by waving their whip-like hairs. There are often so many of them that the water turns green in the summer. These minute plants provide food for many tiny animals, and also for some larger ones like the freshwater mussels. The latter simply draw in currents of water and filter out the algae.

Caddis Fly Cases

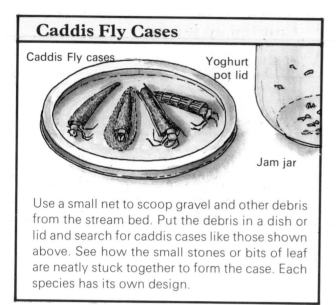

Caddis Fly cases

Yoghurt pot lid

Jam jar

Use a small net to scoop gravel and other debris from the stream bed. Put the debris in a dish or lid and search for caddis cases like those shown above. See how the small stones or bits of leaf are neatly stuck together to form the case. Each species has its own design.

Animals of the Pond

Even a small pond contains hundreds of different kinds of animals. There are plant-eaters and predators, and each kind occupies its own particular niche in the pond environment. Many of the animals can be seen properly only with the aid of a microscope, but they exist in immense numbers and play a vital role in feeding the larger animals.

The best way to collect and study pond dwellers is to use a small net and a number of shallow dishes. But before you start churning up the water with your net, take a few minutes to look at the whole pond environment. Look out for dragonflies flashing through the air with wings rustling as they hunt for flies. Swallows and martins may also swoop low over the water to snatch up the flies, and the grey wagtail often flits nimbly around the water's edge to capture insects. Have a good look, too, at the water surface, for several insects actually live and feed here. As they skate about and capture other insects that fall on to the pond, they are kept up by surface tension – a sort of elastic skin on the surface of the water. The pond skaters are the best-known of these surface-dwellers, but they are shy insects and will skid rapidly for cover if alarmed. Approach very carefully if you want to watch them, and then you might be able to pick out the little dimple that each

foot makes in the water surface. Keep an eye open for the whirligig beetles as well – shiny black beetles that skim round and round on the surface like tiny clockwork toys. You will also see other beetles, together with pond snails and water bugs, rising to the surface every now and then to renew their air supplies. These creatures are rather like scuba-divers, taking their air supplies down with them in containers of various kinds. The snails have lung-like cavities inside their bodies, while water beetles carry their air in the space between the body and the tough wing cases.

When you start to explore below the surface, sweep your net gently to and fro through the water and empty it into a dish of

From Tadpole to Frog

Collect a small amount of frogspawn from a pond and put it in an aquarium with pond water and plenty of water plants. Watch how the eggs gradually change shape as the tadpoles develop. How long do they take to hatch? Watch the baby tadpoles feed on the plants at first. Later they will need animal food. Give them *small* pieces of meat— attached to cotton so that you can pull the remains of the meat out easily before it goes bad. Release the tadpoles back into the pond as soon as all four legs have appeared, for it is very difficult to feed the young frogs at this stage.

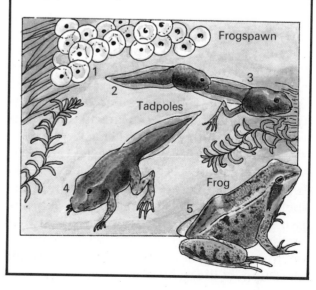

Frogspawn

Tadpoles

Frog

In the Water-weeds

pond water after every couple of sweeps. Take samples from near the surface, from midwater, and from the bottom, and check the kinds of animals in each one. You probably won't find much difference in the first two samples, but the bottom sample will contain many crawling animals that are absent from the other two samples. Don't be surprised to see clusters of leaf fragments or small twigs moving across the bottom of your dish. Look closely and you will see an insect grub poking out from the front of each cluster. The grub is a young caddis fly and it uses the twig or leaf fragments to make a portable house: the fragments are stuck to a tube of silk which the grub spins from its own body. Mayfly nymphs, easily recognized by their three slender 'tails', crawl over or burrow in the mud as a rule, but some swim quite actively. Dragonfly nymphs are fierce predators, shooting out their spiny jaws to catch other animals: they will even attack small fishes. The great diving beetle is another powerful predator.

Newts can be found in the ponds mainly in the spring, when the males are dressed in bright courtship colours and sport frilly crests on their backs and tails. Watch how the males dance around the plumper and less showy females and quiver their tails. Later you might see the females laying their eggs: each one is laid singly and carefully wrapped in a leaf. Newts are amphibians, like the frogs and toads, and the youngsters spend several months in the water as tadpoles.

Small ponds do not usually contain many fish species, although there may be large numbers of individuals. Fishes obtain their oxygen direct from the water by means of their gills and they do not come to the surface for air. Most of them are rather active animals and they need plenty of oxygen, especially when there is a lot of rotting vegetation. The few fishes that can tolerate pond conditions include sticklebacks, perch and carp. The last two species often remain very small through overcrowding. Larger lakes, with plenty of open water, produce much bigger fishes and also support many more species.

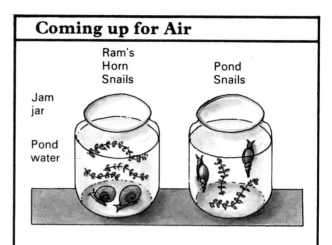

Coming up for Air

Collect two or three great pond snails and the same number of ram's horn snails. Put them in separate jam jars of pond water and watch them carefully for half an hour. How many visits do the snails make to the surface to renew their air supplies? Just count the total visits without noting the individual snails. You will find that the ram's horns do not come up much at all. Their bodies contain haemoglobin – the red pigment that occurs in our blood – and this helps them to absorb oxygen direct from the water. Pond snails have no haemoglobin and cannot absorb much oxygen from the water: they have to surface frequently for air.

Examine the Water-weeds

Many pond and lake animals spend their lives crawling among the water-weeds. You might dislodge some with your net, but a better way of collecting these animals is to drag out a few weeds and examine them in a dish. Look for water beetles and mayfly nymphs attached to the weeds, and notice the large claws which give them a secure grip. Small leeches may stretch and contract as they loop their way over the vegetation. Sausage-shaped blobs of jelly are the egg masses of water snails. Look also for the fascinating *Hydra*, a tiny freshwater relative of the sea anemones. Only a few millimetres long, it attaches itself mainly to the underside of leaves and its slender tentacles dangle in the water to catch water fleas or other small animals that bump into them. The victims are held fast by the hydra's stinging harpoons.

Fishing for Worms

The pond is full of scavenging creatures, which you can catch quite easily by tying a piece of meat to a length of string and hanging it in the water. Pull it out after about 15 minutes and examine it. The most common animals will be small dark flatworms. Put them into a dish of pond water to watch them at work.

Little black or brown animals glide smoothly over the water plants like pieces of ribbon. These are flatworms and they feed on a wide range of living and dead matter. You can also find them on the bottom of the pond, and they even glide upside-down beneath the water surface. A good way to collect these creatures is to hang a piece of meat in the pond for a while (see left). Flatworms have amazing powers of survival and recovery. They can survive without food for months, although they get smaller and smaller during this time, and if you cut them in half each piece will quickly grow into a new animal. In fact, you can cut them into dozens of pieces and each piece will grow. What is more, each piece 'remembers' which was the front and always grows its new head at the right end.

Life in the River

As we have already seen, a river varies a great deal from place to place along its course. Each stretch, or reach, has its own assortment of wildlife. The lowland reach, where the water moves quite slowly, is very similar to the lowland lake or pond, although there are more kinds of fish in the river. Bream, tench, perch, roach, rudd and pike all occur regularly in the

Set up an Aquarium

You can keep many pond creatures at home in a simple glass or plastic aquarium. Put some clean sand or gravel and a few stones on the bottom of the tank (not a fish bowl), together with a few plants. Stand the tank in the light, but not in the full sun and fill it with pond water. Sticklebacks do well in a simple aquarium, and you can add most of the common pond creatures as well, but avoid dragonfly nymphs and the great diving beetle: these will eat the other animals. Add water fleas from time to time to feed the fishes.

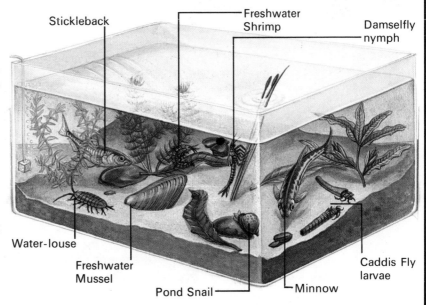

Stickleback

Freshwater Shrimp

Damselfly nymph

Water-louse

Freshwater Mussel

Pond Snail

Minnow

Caddis Fly larvae

lowland river, and there are often many eels as well. Canals are also very similar to lakes and lowland rivers. All these waters have rather muddy bottoms, with plenty of water weeds and many emergent plants along the edges.

Further upstream, however, in the minnow reach and the troutbeck, the conditions are very different. The swift currents of the troutbeck scour the river bed and carry away all the small stones and mud. Few plants can establish themselves at the water's edge, and none at all grow in the middle. Only strong swimmers can maintain themselves in the open water, and the trout is obviously the main fish living here. Loach and miller's thumb stay close to the bottom, where the current is a little slower, and minnows sometimes manage to live in some of the quieter pools along the margins. Try measuring the speed of the current by throwing a twig into the middle and timing it over 50 or 100 metres.

There is plenty of insect life on the bottom of the stream, feeding mainly on plant debris carried down by the current. The mayfly nymphs living here are very flat, quite unlike the burrowing forms living in lakes and ponds, and they cling tightly to the stones so that they are not dislodged by the current. Stonefly nymphs are also found here. They resemble mayfly nymphs in many ways, but have only two 'tails'. Look for the fragile empty skins on the waterside stones, showing where the nymphs have crawled out of the water, split their skins and pulled themselves out as adult insects.

Many caddis flies breed in the swift currents of the troutbeck and minnow reach, but instead of using plant fragments to make their cases the larvae use small stones. The stones weigh the insects down and prevent them from being washed away. The larva of *Anabolia* always attaches some small sticks to its case: these probably protect the larvae from the trout, which gobble up most kinds of caddis grubs, but they also have another function. Search for some occupied cases on the stream bed. Notice how they all lie with the head end facing upstream. The twigs help to line them up in this way, and then debris drifting along the stream bed is brought right to the larval mouths. A few caddis grubs

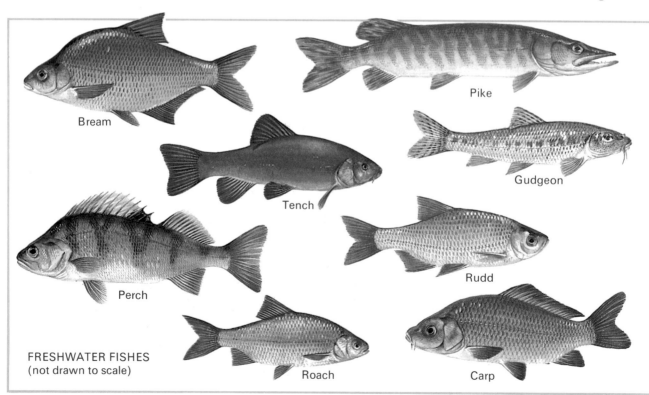

Bream

Pike

Tench

Gudgeon

Perch

Rudd

Roach

Carp

FRESHWATER FISHES
(not drawn to scale)

Waterside Bird-watching

The Aggressive Stickleback

Capture a male stickleback in the spring at the beginning of the breeding season. You can easily distinguish the males by the red throat and belly. Put your fish in a small aquarium with some gravel and plenty of water plants. He defends his territory very vigorously and, in nature, drives away any other male stickleback. Put a small mirror in the aquarium and watch the fish attack his own reflection in the belief that it is another male.

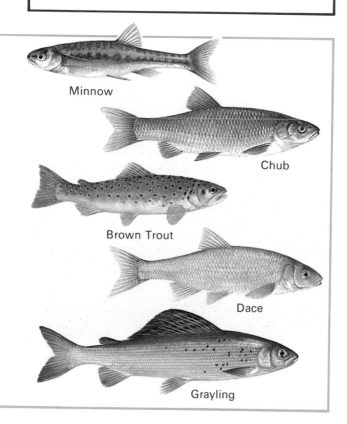

Minnow

Chub

Brown Trout

Dace

Grayling

cement their cases permanently to large stones on the river bed.

The current is a little slower in the minnow reach which is also known as the grayling reach on the continent because there the grayling is especially common in this zone. Banks of gravel build up here and there, especially on the insides of bends, and various plants are able to establish themselves. The current flows faster around the outsides of the bends, eroding the banks more quickly and cutting deeper channels. This is where you should look for the fishes. Gudgeon and chub live here as well as the minnows and grayling. Trout spawn on the beds of gravel, and salmon also spawn in this zone in some rivers. Here, too, the colourful male stickleback makes his tunnel-shaped nest by gluing bits of weed together with secretion from his body. He then attracts a female with an intricate courtship dance and leads her to his nest. After she has laid her eggs, the male looks after them and the babies when they hatch.

Dace, roach and rudd begin to appear as you move down towards the lowland reach. Keep your eyes open for the crayfish which looks like a small brown lobster. It lurks under stones by day and comes out to catch other animals at night.

Waterside Bird-watching

The banks of both still and moving waters are excellent habitats for birds. Look for the beautiful kingfisher all the way along the river from the troutbeck down. As long as it has a suitable perch from which to watch the water it will be able to dive in and catch small fishes. But this bird also needs a good bank somewhere in which to dig its nest burrow. You are most likely to see the dipper on the upper parts of the river, perching on boulders and bobbing up and down on midstream stones. Then it disappears by simply walking into the water. Under the surface it can walk or swim while searching for caddis grubs and other insects. The heron prefers to fish in quieter waters with plenty of vegetation around the edges. Look for it in the lowland

29

Identifying Birds

WATERSIDE BIRDS

Moorhen

Grey Wagtail

Reed Warbler

summer

winter

Little Egret

winter

Dabchick

summer

Dipper

Kingfisher

Coot

female

male

Marsh Harrier

female

male

Reed Bunting

reach of the river and also around canals and lakes. It catches frogs and other animals as well as fishes.

It is a good idea to build a simple hide close to a pond or a lake, or a slow-moving river, for many birds live here and stay in more or less one place for long periods. Make it with a frame of branches covered with an old sheet dyed green and a few leafy twigs, and be prepared to sit in it quietly for long periods. From your hide you will be able to watch swans, ducks, coots, moorhens and grebes, among other interesting birds. Some of the birds are illustrated above. Many of them nest among the waterside vegetation, or even on rafts of dead plants. Watch the ducks feeding. There are two main groups. The mallard belongs to the group known as dabbling ducks: they feed by putting their heads into the water or by up-ending themselves and

Above: A female mallard takes her brood of ducklings for a swim. The ducklings are able to swim almost as soon as they hatch from the eggs.

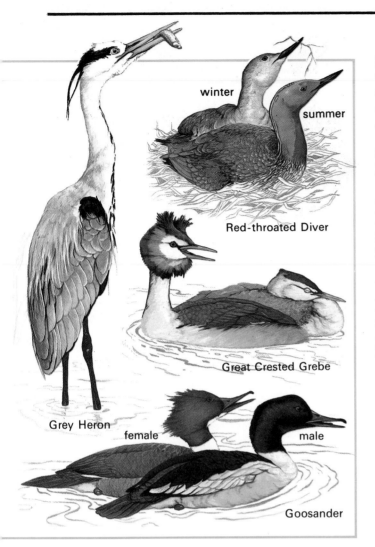

winter

summer

Red-throated Diver

Great Crested Grebe

Grey Heron

female

male

Goosander

Binoculars by the Water

Ducks and other water birds often swim far out on lakes or on the sea, so you will need binoculars to identify them and to study them properly. Choose a fairly powerful pair if you are likely to do most of your bird-watching by the water. A practical size is 9×40 which magnifies 9 times but is still not too heavy. Another good size is 8×40, but if you can afford a light-weight pair choose 10×24 or 10×30. These will give you a better magnification with less weight, but they are not so useful at dusk because the small objective lenses, only 24 or 30 millimetres across, do not let much light through. Keep your binoculars strapped around your neck at all times so that they can't fall into the water. Practise following birds in flight with your binoculars but be very careful not to point them at the sun as this could blind you.

leaving just the tail sticking out of the water. The other group are known as diving ducks. They feed by diving right under the surface. The tufted duck is a typical diving duck. Watch to find out what sort of things both groups of duck eat – apart from the bread that people like to give them.

Winter is a very good time for watching ducks in Britain and other parts of western Europe, for huge numbers fly in from the north when their ponds and lakes start to freeze over. Many geese and swans come too.

Under the Ice

Have you ever wondered what happens to fishes and other aquatic animals when their ponds freeze over in the winter? In fact, the ice forms an insulating blanket for the lower layers, and the water at the bottom usually remains well above freezing point. Life can carry on almost as normal, although everything slows down as the temperature falls. Fishes become very lethargic and spend most of their time sitting quietly on the bottom. Many other creatures do the same, but some of the smaller animals go into a true resting stage, surrounded by a thick coat which can resist very low temperatures. Because they move very little, the animals require little oxygen: there is usually enough dissolved in the water to keep them going, and as long as the ice is not too thick or covered with snow the submerged plants can continue to make food by photosynthesis, with the consequent release of more oxygen.

Plants which float at or near the surface in summer often sink to the bottom in winter. The duckweed stores a lot of starch in the autumn and its thalli become swollen and heavy. They sink to the bottom of the pond, but by the end of the winter they have used up much of the stored food and they are light enough to float up again and resume normal life. In very cold winters the ice may exceed 15 centimetres in depth, but it rarely exceeds 25 centimetres in Britain. So if your garden pond is at least 50 centimetres deep in the centre, there will always be some free water for your fishes.

Index

SEASHORE PONDS AND STREAMS

This edition published in 1993 by Rainbow Books,
Elsley House, 24–30 Great Titchfield Street, London W1P 7AD

Originally published in 1985

10 9 8 7 6 5 4 3 2 1

Text copyright © Michael Chinery 1985
Illustrations copyright © Grisewood & Dempsey Ltd 1985

All rights reserved. No part of this publication may be
reproduced, stored in a retrieval system or transmitted by any
means, electronic, mechanical, photocopying or otherwise,
without the prior permission of the publisher.

ISBN 1 85698 012 X

Printed in Italy